© SKOGSLIV
The Owl Goes on Holiday
Project manager: Lena Allblom, IKEA of Sweden AB
Project coordinator: Anders Truedsson, TITEL Books AB
Text: Ulf Stark
Illustrations: Ann-Cathrine Sigrid Ståhlberg
Layout: Ann-Cathrine Sigrid Ståhlberg
Typesetting: Gyllene Snittet AB, Sweden
Translation: Comactiva Language Partner AB, Sweden
Produced by IKEA of Sweden AB
Paper: Arcoset FSC
Printing: Litopat S.p.A., Italy 2015

We aim to provide as much inspiration as possible, but with minimal impact on the environment. All our books take the environment into account in every stage of production, from the choice of paper to how we distribute our printed material.

The book you are holding is printed on paper that meets all the requirements for responsible forestry. This means, for example, that the paper raw material comes from trees that are certified to originate from a sustainably managed forest. We print using vegetable-based printing inks without solvents, and the printers are located close to our large markets to avoid long-distance transport to you.

We are also working to develop the printed medium so that it minimises impact on the environment in the future. Read more about our environmental work at www.ikea.co.uk

MIX
Paper from responsible sources
FSC® C018744

The Owl
Goes on Holiday

Ulf Stark
Ann-Cathrine Sigrid Ståhlberg

By the big stone under the oak tree, the owl gives school lessons
to the children of the forest.

He does this every morning before going to bed. Because owls
sleep in the daytime and are awake at night.

Today the children have picked leaves, needles and pine cones from
the trees. They have also held paws and wings around the oak tree to see
how wide it is.

"As wide as all of us put together," says the owl.

"My grandad is quite wide too," says the smallest little mouse.

"But the oak tree could live for over a thousand years," says the owl.
"I don't think your grandad could. Or me!"

They all laugh at that. Then they dance around the oak tree, because
dancing is so much fun. And because you learn a lot better when you're
having fun.

Now the owl stands on the school stone and shows the class a leaf.

"Does anybody know what this is?"

"Can I have a look, please," says the hare, stretching out his paw.

He takes the leaf, puts it straight in his mouth and eats it up.

"A maple leaf," he says, licking his lips.

"Correct," says the owl. "But you mustn't keep eating what we are learning about."

"Sorry," says the hare. "But I was so hungry."

"So am I," says the little girl squirrel.

And she jumps up and grabs a pine cone the owl was just going to show the class, and starts gnawing on it.

"Yucky pine cones," says the fox. "I much prefer…"

"Flies!" croaks the frog.

"Snails," says the hedgehog.

"Spiders are quite nice," says the magpie.

"I was going to say hares," says the fox, leering at the hare.

"Different animals like to eat different things," says the owl. "Personally, I like…"

"Us!" squeak the mice.

And they jump around squeaking:

"Ha ha, you're not allowed to eat us up. Not while we're at school!"

Because that is the way of things – at school everybody has to be kind to each other and not eat each other up.

"Now I think it's time for you to do some exercise," yawns the owl. "Move around as much as you can."

The owl is tired. It is fun that the children are so lively. But it's also very tiring, especially if you haven't had much sleep. And the owl has not been sleeping well at all. For several days, a woodpecker has been pecking away at a fir tree next to the oak where the owl sleeps.

And owls have EXCELLENT hearing.

Imagine if I could have just a few days off, he thinks to himself.

He looks at the mice, who have found an acorn and are playing football. The hare jumps over the hedgehog. And the squirrel jumps around from tree to tree.

In a while I will teach them to count to four, he thinks.

And then he gives another big yawn, and falls asleep.

"Wake up owl!" caws the magpie.

"Hoo-hoo," hoots the owl. "What's the matter?"

"You fell asleep," says the magpie. "School has finished."

Everybody is looking at him. The pupils. And their parents who have come to take them home. He has never fallen asleep in a lesson before.

"I'm so sorry," he says. "I must have dropped off for a few minutes. That's it for today, thank you. You can go home now."

"Excuse me," says mummy mouse. "I'm not very good at counting. Are all four of my children here?"

"Yes they are," says the owl. "Let's see… One, two, three, four."

And off she and the other parents go with their children. Only the magpie stays behind.

"You should have a rest," she says. "You should go on holiday."

"Holiday? What's a holiday?" wonders the owl.

"Don't you know?" caws the magpie.

"Not really," replies the owl.

So the magpie explains:

"Holiday is when you fly off somewhere else. You rest, have a good time and just do nothing in particular. Just sleep, eat and have fun."

"That sounds nice," sighs the owl. "But how will the young animals learn anything?"

"I can be the teacher," suggests the magpie.

"You? What are you good at?"

"Oh, various things," says the magpie.

"It certainly would be nice," says the owl. "But you must make sure they learn to count to four. And build a nest."

"Trust me! Have a nice sleep today and you can set off this evening."

Before the owl creeps into his hole, he puts four sticks next to each other by the school stone.

"This is four. See? One, two, three, four. Just so you don't forget."

"Okay," caws the magpie.

And that evening, the owl sets off. He flies to the other side of the forest, where he finds another hole. Smaller than his usual one, but it is only a holiday home. When he has finished eating, he sits on a branch and enjoys doing nothing.

He breathes in the smells of the forest. He sees the bats swooping by, and hears the mosquitoes buzzing. In fact, he can even hear a spider weaving its web. Because as we know, owls have excellent hearing.

How lovely and restful this is, he thinks. I think I am going to enjoy it here.

"Good morning children!" caws the magpie next morning. "I am your new teacher."

"But where's the owl?" wonders the hare.

"He has gone on holiday. Let's get started!"

"What are we doing today?" asks the squirrel.

"Today, you are going to learn how to build a nest," says the magpie.

"I already live in a little passageway under the ground," says one of the mice.

"But now you're going to learn how to build the best nest of all. A real magpie's nest," caws the magpie proudly.

Everybody helps out. Voles and mice fetch small twigs. The hare and the fox bring big branches. And the frog carries mud for the floor.

The magpie shows them how the branches should be put together. They have to really do it properly, otherwise the nest will break.

When the lesson is over, everybody is tired but happy.

"Now you have learned how to build a real nest," says the magpie.

The fox says it would rather live in its den. The hare wants to carry on living in his lovely sleeping burrow under a bush. The squirrel loves her own nest. And the mice have their underground tunnel to live in.

But the children are still happy when their parents come to collect them.

They have had a lot of fun. They have learned to work together. And that all animals want to live in their own kind of home.

"Are all four of my children here?" asks mummy mouse when she is leaving.

The magpie looks at the sticks which the owl put on the ground. Then she looks at the little mice. The same number of sticks and little mice. And the owl said that was four.

"Yes they are," says the magpie. "Everything is all right."

But it isn't all right.

When they were building the nest, one mouse accidentally took one of the sticks for the nest. So now mummy mouse is going home with only three children.

The smallest one has gone missing. He got lost when he went off to fetch a twig.

The owl is having trouble sleeping in his new hole. He thinks it's a shame to be sleeping when he's on holiday.

He thinks about how nice it is not to have the mice squeaking, the frog croaking and the woodpecker pecking.

This is really, really nice, he thinks. I don't have to work, I can do just what I like.

The trouble is, he doesn't really know what it is that he wants.

All day long, he thinks about what he wants.

And all night long, he flies around thinking the same thing. He looks at all the same things as he looked at when he first arrived. But it doesn't feel as exciting any more.

When the sun finally rises over the treetops, he realises what he wants. HE WANTS TO GET BACK TO HIS SCHOOLCHILDREN!

This morning's lesson has begun. Today the magpie wants to teach everybody to fly. Some already can. But the others have no idea what to do.

"You have to really flap a lot," the magpie explains.

One after one they have to stand on the school stone.

"Don't be scared! Jump off and flap as hard as you can."

The hare tries to flap his ears, the fox tries to flap its legs, and the little mice spin their tails round and round. But they all just fall as soon as they jump.

They laugh at that, because falling over is fun.

Just then, along comes the owl.

"How clever of you," he says to the magpie. "I see that you're teaching the children that no one can do everything. But everyone can do something. The hare can't fly, but is really good at hopping. The hedgehog can't hop, but is very good at being prickly."

Just then, the owl sees the big magpie's nest they have built.

"And what a lovely schoolhouse you have built! Now we can be indoors whenever we like. Oh, I'm so happy to see you all again… But where is the smallest mouse?"

"The smallest mouse?" caws the magpie. "Yes, where is he?"

"Did you count to make sure mummy mouse collected all her children yesterday?"

"Yes I did," says the magpie. "There were as many little mice as there were sticks there."

"Oh dear," says the owl when he sees the three sticks. "I must fly off and start looking straight away."

He flies over forest glades, streams and meadows. The owl has excellent eyesight, and can zoom in on a single blade of grass. And hear the quietest of noises.

Just now he can hear someone laughing.

Somebody with a very light voice.

It's the smallest mouse. He has been sleeping in a pile of leaves. He has found a dead fly in a spider's web which he has feasted on.

And now he is lying on the ground, tickling himself on the tummy with his tail.

Because he doesn't like to be bored.

"Hoo, there you are!" hoots the owl. "My dear, naughty pupil."

Carefully, he picks up the mouse with his claws and flies back to the school.

"What lesson are we going to have now?" wonder the children when the owl returns.

"We are going to have music! We are celebrating because we have a new schoolhouse, I am back from my holiday, and because we have found the smallest mouse," says the owl.

And they all go into the schoolhouse and sing as loudly as they can.

All except the smallest mouse. He is hanging upside-down from a branch by his tail. He is swinging back and forth and thinking: What a good job the owl found me. Tomorrow I am going to learn to count to four, just to be on the safe side.